NAME:

ADVENTURE

RV LOGBOOK

"Travel makes one modest.
You see what a tiny place
you occupy in the World."
–Gustave Flaubert

RV LOG

DATE: ☀ ⛅ ☁ 🌧 ⛈ ❄ 🌬 ☐Hot ☐Cold ☐Mild

Traveled from _____ to _____

Route Taken: _____

Start Mileage: _____ End Mileage: _____ Total Miles Traveled: _____

Sites Along The Way: _____

CAMPGROUND ☆☆☆☆☆

Campground Name: _____

Address: _____

Phone: _____ GPS: _____

Site #: _____ Ideal Site # (for next time): _____

Cost: _____ ☐ day ☐ week ☐ month

Memberships: _____

Altitude: _____ ☐ First Visit ☐ Return Visit

DRIVEWAY LENGTH: _____

☐easy access   ☐back-in   ☐antenna reception
☐loop   ☐pull-through   ☐satellite tv
☐paved   ☐restrooms   ☐cable tv
☐unpaved-graded   ☐pet friendly   ☐wifi:
☐picnic table   ☐shade-partial/full   ☐free ☐$____
☐fire ring   ☐full sun   cell phone carrier:
☐water   ☐laundry
☐sewer   ☐store/visitor center _____
☐electricity   ☐pool/hot tub   phone reception
☐15 amp   ☐hiking trails   ☆☆☆☆☆
☐30 amp   ☐fishing   water pressure
☐50 amp   ☐firewood   ☆☆☆☆☆

NOTES FOR NEXT TIME
(fees, check in/out times, discounts, directions, loud/quiet, etc)

NOTES

(Campground Pros/Cons, Traveling Companions, People Met, Places Visited,
Things to Do, Restaurants, Journaling):

RV LOG

DATE: ☀ ⛅ ☁ 🌧 ⛈ ❄ 🌬 ☐Hot ☐Cold ☐Mild

Traveled from _____ to _____

Route Taken: _____

Start Mileage: _____ End Mileage: _____ Total Miles Traveled: _____

Sites Along The Way:

CAMPGROUND ☆☆☆☆☆

Campground Name: _____

Address: _____

Phone: _____ GPS: _____

Site #: _____ Ideal Site # (for next time): _____

Cost: _____ ☐ day ☐ week ☐ month

Memberships: _____

Altitude: _____ ☐ First Visit ☐ Return Visit

DRIVEWAY LENGTH:

☐easy access   ☐back-in   ☐antenna reception
☐loop   ☐pull-through   ☐satellite tv
☐paved   ☐restrooms   ☐cable tv
☐unpaved-graded   ☐pet friendly   ☐wifi:
☐picnic table   ☐shade-partial/full   ☐free ☐$____
☐fire ring   ☐full sun   cell phone carrier:
☐water   ☐laundry
☐sewer   ☐store/visitor center   _____
☐electricity   ☐pool/hot tub   phone reception
☐15 amp   ☐hiking trails   ☆☆☆☆☆
☐30 amp   ☐fishing   water pressure
☐50 amp   ☐firewood   ☆☆☆☆☆

NOTES FOR NEXT TIME

(fees, check in/out times, discounts, directions, loud/quiet, etc)

NOTES

(Campground Pros/Cons, Traveling Companions, People Met, Places Visited, Things to Do, Restaurants, Journaling):

RV LOG

DATE: ☀ ⛅ ☁ 🌧 ⛈ ❄ 🌬 ☐Hot ☐Cold ☐Mild

Traveled from _____ to _____

Route Taken: _____

Start Mileage: _____ End Mileage: _____ Total Miles Traveled: _____

Sites Along The Way: _____

CAMPGROUND ☆☆☆☆☆

Campground Name: _____

Address: _____

Phone: _____ GPS: _____

Site #: _____ Ideal Site # (for next time): _____

Cost: _____ ☐ day ☐ week ☐ month

Memberships: _____

Altitude: _____ ☐ First Visit ☐ Return Visit

DRIVEWAY LENGTH:

☐easy access   ☐back-in   ☐antenna reception
☐loop   ☐pull-through   ☐satellite tv
☐paved   ☐restrooms   ☐cable tv
☐unpaved-graded   ☐pet friendly   ☐wifi:
☐picnic table   ☐shade-partial/full   ☐free ☐$____
☐fire ring   ☐full sun
☐water   ☐laundry   **cell phone carrier:**
☐sewer   ☐store/visitor center
☐electricity   ☐pool/hot tub   _____
☐15 amp   ☐hiking trails   **phone reception**
☐30 amp   ☐fishing   ☆☆☆☆☆
☐50 amp   ☐firewood   **water pressure**
   ☆☆☆☆☆

NOTES FOR NEXT TIME

(fees, check in/out times, discounts, directions, loud/quiet, etc)

NOTES

(Campground Pros/Cons, Traveling Companions, People Met, Places Visited, Things to Do, Restaurants, Journaling):

RV LOG

DATE: ☼ ⛅ ☁ ☂ ⚡ ❄ 🌬 ☐Hot ☐Cold ☐Mild

Traveled from _____ to _____

Route Taken: _____

Start Mileage: _____ End Mileage: _____ Total Miles Traveled: _____

Sites Along The Way: _____

CAMPGROUND ☆☆☆☆☆

Campground Name: _____

Address: _____

Phone: _____ GPS: _____

Site #: _____ Ideal Site # (for next time): _____

Cost: _____ ☐ day ☐ week ☐ month

Memberships: _____

Altitude: _____ ☐ First Visit ☐ Return Visit

DRIVEWAY LENGTH:

☐ easy access   ☐ back-in   ☐ antenna reception
☐ loop   ☐ pull-through   ☐ satellite tv
☐ paved   ☐ restrooms   ☐ cable tv
☐ unpaved-graded   ☐ pet friendly   ☐ wifi:
☐ picnic table   ☐ shade-partial/full   ☐ free ☐$_____
☐ fire ring   ☐ full sun   cell phone carrier:
☐ water   ☐ laundry
☐ sewer   ☐ store/visitor center   _____
☐ electricity   ☐ pool/hot tub   phone reception
☐ 15 amp   ☐ hiking trails   ☆☆☆☆☆
☐ 30 amp   ☐ fishing   water pressure
☐ 50 amp   ☐ firewood   ☆☆☆☆☆

NOTES FOR NEXT TIME

(fees, check in/out times, discounts, directions, loud/quiet, etc)

NOTES

(Campground Pros/Cons, Traveling Companions, People Met, Places Visited,
Things to Do, Restaurants, Journaling):

RV LOG

DATE: ☀ ⛅ ☁ 🌧 ⛈ ❄ 🌫 ☐Hot ☐Cold ☐Mild

Traveled from _____ to _____

Route Taken: _____

Start Mileage: _____ End Mileage: _____ Total Miles Traveled: _____

Sites Along The Way: _____

CAMPGROUND ☆ ☆ ☆ ☆ ☆

Campground Name: _____

Address: _____

Phone: _____ GPS: _____

Site #: _____ Ideal Site # (for next time): _____

Cost: _____ ☐ day ☐ week ☐ month

Memberships: _____

Altitude: _____ ☐ First Visit ☐ Return Visit

DRIVEWAY LENGTH:

☐ easy access ☐ back-in ☐ antenna reception
☐ loop ☐ pull-through ☐ satellite tv
☐ paved ☐ restrooms ☐ cable tv
☐ unpaved-graded ☐ pet friendly ☐ wifi:
☐ picnic table ☐ shade-partial/full ☐ free ☐$_____
☐ fire ring ☐ full sun cell phone carrier:
☐ water ☐ laundry _____
☐ sewer ☐ store/visitor center
☐ electricity ☐ pool/hot tub phone reception
☐ 15 amp ☐ hiking trails ☆ ☆ ☆ ☆ ☆
☐ 30 amp ☐ fishing water pressure
☐ 50 amp ☐ firewood ☆ ☆ ☆ ☆ ☆

NOTES FOR NEXT TIME

(fees, check in/out times, discounts, directions, loud/quiet, etc)

NOTES

(Campground Pros/Cons, Traveling Companions, People Met, Places Visited,
Things to Do, Restaurants, Journaling):

RV LOG

DATE: ☀ ⛅ ☁ 🌧 ⛈ ❄ 🌫 ☐Hot ☐Cold ☐Mild

Traveled from _____ to _____

Route Taken: _____

Start Mileage: _____ End Mileage: _____ Total Miles Traveled: _____

Sites Along The Way: _____

CAMPGROUND ☆☆☆☆☆

Campground Name: _____

Address: _____

Phone: _____ GPS: _____

Site #: _____ Ideal Site # (for next time): _____

Cost: _____ ☐ day ☐ week ☐ month

Memberships: _____

Altitude: _____ ☐ First Visit ☐ Return Visit

DRIVEWAY LENGTH:

☐ easy access ☐ back-in ☐ antenna reception
☐ loop ☐ pull-through ☐ satellite tv
☐ paved ☐ restrooms ☐ cable tv
☐ unpaved-graded ☐ pet friendly ☐ wifi:
☐ picnic table ☐ shade-partial/full   ☐ free ☐ $_____
☐ fire ring ☐ full sun
☐ water ☐ laundry   **cell phone carrier:**
☐ sewer ☐ store/visitor center _____
☐ electricity ☐ pool/hot tub   **phone reception**
☐ 15 amp ☐ hiking trails ☆☆☆☆☆
☐ 30 amp ☐ fishing   **water pressure**
☐ 50 amp ☐ firewood ☆☆☆☆☆

NOTES FOR NEXT TIME

(fees, check in/out times, discounts, directions, loud/quiet, etc)

NOTES

(Campground Pros/Cons, Traveling Companions, People Met, Places Visited, Things to Do, Restaurants, Journaling):

RV LOG

DATE: ☀ ⛅ ☁ ☂ ☔ ⚡ ❄ 🌫 ☐Hot ☐Cold ☐Mild

Traveled from _____ to _____

Route Taken: _____

Start Mileage: _____ End Mileage: _____ Total Miles Traveled: _____

Sites Along The Way: _____

CAMPGROUND ☆☆☆☆☆

Campground Name: _____

Address: _____

Phone: _____ GPS: _____

Site #: _____ Ideal Site # (for next time): _____

Cost: _____ ☐ day ☐ week ☐ month

Memberships: _____

Altitude: _____ ☐ First Visit ☐ Return Visit

DRIVEWAY LENGTH:

☐easy access ☐back-in ☐antenna reception
☐loop ☐pull-through ☐satellite tv
☐paved ☐restrooms ☐cable tv
☐unpaved-graded ☐pet friendly ☐wifi:
☐picnic table ☐shade-partial/full   ☐free ☐$____
☐fire ring ☐full sun cell phone carrier:
☐water ☐laundry
☐sewer ☐store/visitor center _____
☐electricity ☐pool/hot tub phone reception
☐15 amp ☐hiking trails ☆☆☆☆☆
☐30 amp ☐fishing water pressure
☐50 amp ☐firewood ☆☆☆☆☆

NOTES FOR NEXT TIME

(fees, check in/out times, discounts, directions, loud/quiet, etc)

NOTES

(Campground Pros/Cons, Traveling Companions, People Met, Places Visited, Things to Do, Restaurants, Journaling):

RV LOG

DATE: ☀ ⛅ ☁ 🌧 ⛈ ❄ 🌫 ☐Hot ☐Cold ☐Mild

Traveled from _____ to _____

Route Taken: _____

Start Mileage: _____ End Mileage: _____ Total Miles Traveled: _____

Sites Along The Way: _____

CAMPGROUND ☆☆☆☆☆

Campground Name: _____

Address: _____

Phone: _____ GPS: _____

Site #: _____ Ideal Site # (for next time): _____

Cost: _____ ☐ day ☐ week ☐ month

Memberships: _____

Altitude: _____ ☐ First Visit ☐ Return Visit

DRIVEWAY LENGTH:

☐ easy access
☐ loop
☐ paved
☐ unpaved-graded
☐ picnic table
☐ fire ring
☐ water
☐ sewer
☐ electricity
☐ 15 amp
☐ 30 amp
☐ 50 amp

☐ back-in
☐ pull-through
☐ restrooms
☐ pet friendly
☐ shade-partial/full
☐ full sun
☐ laundry
☐ store/visitor center
☐ pool/hot tub
☐ hiking trails
☐ fishing
☐ firewood

☐ antenna reception
☐ satellite tv
☐ cable tv
☐ wifi:
  ☐ free ☐ $_____

cell phone carrier:
_____

phone reception
☆☆☆☆☆
water pressure
☆☆☆☆☆

NOTES FOR NEXT TIME

(fees, check in/out times, discounts, directions, loud/quiet, etc)

NOTES

(Campground Pros/Cons, Traveling Companions, People Met, Places Visited,
Things to Do, Restaurants, Journaling):

RV LOG

DATE: ☀ ⛅ ☁ 🌧 ⛈ ❄ 🌫 ☐Hot ☐Cold ☐Mild

Traveled from _____ to _____

Route Taken: _____

Start Mileage: _____ End Mileage: _____ Total Miles Traveled: _____

Sites Along The Way: _____

CAMPGROUND ☆☆☆☆☆

Campground Name: _____

Address: _____

Phone: _____ GPS: _____

Site #: _____ Ideal Site # (for next time): _____

Cost: _____ ☐ day ☐ week ☐ month

Memberships: _____

Altitude: _____ ☐ First Visit ☐ Return Visit

DRIVEWAY LENGTH:

☐ easy access
☐ loop
☐ paved
☐ unpaved-graded
☐ picnic table
☐ fire ring
☐ water
☐ sewer
☐ electricity
☐ 15 amp
☐ 30 amp
☐ 50 amp

☐ back-in
☐ pull-through
☐ restrooms
☐ pet friendly
☐ shade-partial/full
☐ full sun
☐ laundry
☐ store/visitor center
☐ pool/hot tub
☐ hiking trails
☐ fishing
☐ firewood

☐ antenna reception
☐ satellite tv
☐ cable tv
☐ wifi:
  ☐ free ☐ $_____

cell phone carrier:
_____

phone reception
☆☆☆☆☆
water pressure
☆☆☆☆☆

NOTES FOR NEXT TIME

(fees, check in/out times, discounts, directions, loud/quiet, etc)

NOTES

(Campground Pros/Cons, Traveling Companions, People Met, Places Visited,
Things to Do, Restaurants, Journaling):

RV LOG

DATE: ☀ ⛅ ☁ 🌧 ⛈ ❄ 🌬 ☐Hot ☐Cold ☐Mild

Traveled from .... to ....

Route Taken: ....

Start Mileage: .... End Mileage: .... Total Miles Traveled: ....

Sites Along The Way:

CAMPGROUND ☆ ☆ ☆ ☆ ☆

Campground Name: ....

Address: ....

Phone: .... GPS: ....

Site #: .... Ideal Site # (for next time): ....

Cost: .... ☐ day   ☐ week   ☐ month

Memberships: ....

Altitude: ....   ☐ First Visit   ☐ Return Visit

DRIVEWAY LENGTH:

☐ easy access
☐ loop
☐ paved
☐ unpaved-graded
☐ picnic table
☐ fire ring
☐ water
☐ sewer
☐ electricity
☐ 15 amp
☐ 30 amp
☐ 50 amp

☐ back-in
☐ pull-through
☐ restrooms
☐ pet friendly
☐ shade-partial/full
☐ full sun
☐ laundry
☐ store/visitor center
☐ pool/hot tub
☐ hiking trails
☐ fishing
☐ firewood

☐ antenna reception
☐ satellite tv
☐ cable tv
☐ wifi:
  ☐ free ☐ $ _____

cell phone carrier:

_____

phone reception
☆ ☆ ☆ ☆ ☆
water pressure
☆ ☆ ☆ ☆ ☆

NOTES FOR NEXT TIME

(fees, check in/out times, discounts, directions, loud/quiet, etc)

NOTES

(Campground Pros/Cons, Traveling Companions, People Met, Places Visited,
Things to Do, Restaurants, Journaling):

RV LOG

DATE: ☀️ ⛅ ☁️ 🌧️ ⛈️ ❄️ 🌬️ ☐Hot ☐Cold ☐Mild

Traveled from _____ to _____

Route Taken: _____

Start Mileage: _____ End Mileage: _____ Total Miles Traveled: _____

Sites Along The Way: _____

CAMPGROUND ☆☆☆☆☆

Campground Name: _____

Address: _____

Phone: _____ GPS: _____

Site #: _____ Ideal Site # (for next time): _____

Cost: _____ ☐ day ☐ week ☐ month

Memberships: _____

Altitude: _____ ☐ First Visit ☐ Return Visit

DRIVEWAY LENGTH:

☐ easy access   ☐ back-in   ☐ antenna reception
☐ loop   ☐ pull-through   ☐ satellite tv
☐ paved   ☐ restrooms   ☐ cable tv
☐ unpaved-graded   ☐ pet friendly   ☐ wifi:
☐ picnic table   ☐ shade-partial/full   ☐ free ☐ $_____
☐ fire ring   ☐ full sun   **cell phone carrier:**
☐ water   ☐ laundry
☐ sewer   ☐ store/visitor center   _____
☐ electricity   ☐ pool/hot tub   **phone reception**
☐ 15 amp   ☐ hiking trails   ☆☆☆☆☆
☐ 30 amp   ☐ fishing   **water pressure**
☐ 50 amp   ☐ firewood   ☆☆☆☆☆

NOTES FOR NEXT TIME

(fees, check in/out times, discounts, directions, loud/quiet, etc)

NOTES

(Campground Pros/Cons, Traveling Companions, People Met, Places Visited,
Things to Do, Restaurants, Journaling):

RV LOG

DATE: ☀ ⛅ ☁ 🌧 ⛈ ❄ 🌫 ☐Hot ☐Cold ☐Mild

Traveled from _____ to _____

Route Taken: _____

Start Mileage: _____ End Mileage: _____ Total Miles Traveled: _____

Sites Along The Way: _____

CAMPGROUND ☆☆☆☆☆

Campground Name: _____

Address: _____

Phone: _____ GPS: _____

Site #: _____ Ideal Site # (for next time): _____

Cost: _____ ☐ day ☐ week ☐ month

Memberships: _____

Altitude: _____ ☐ First Visit ☐ Return Visit

DRIVEWAY LENGTH:

☐easy access	☐back-in	☐antenna reception
☐loop	☐pull-through	☐satellite tv
☐paved	☐restrooms	☐cable tv
☐unpaved-graded	☐pet friendly	☐wifi:
☐picnic table	☐shade-partial/full	☐free ☐$____
☐fire ring	☐full sun	**cell phone carrier:**
☐water	☐laundry	
☐sewer	☐store/visitor center	_____
☐electricity	☐pool/hot tub	**phone reception**
☐15 amp	☐hiking trails	☆☆☆☆☆
☐30 amp	☐fishing	**water pressure**
☐50 amp	☐firewood	☆☆☆☆☆

NOTES FOR NEXT TIME

(fees, check in/out times, discounts, directions, loud/quiet, etc)

NOTES

(Campground Pros/Cons, Traveling Companions, People Met, Places Visited,
Things to Do, Restaurants, Journaling):

RV LOG

DATE: ☀ ⛅ ☁ 🌧 ⛈ ❄ 🌫 ☐Hot ☐Cold ☐Mild

Traveled from _____ to _____

Route Taken: _____

Start Mileage: _____ End Mileage: _____ Total Miles Traveled: _____

Sites Along The Way: _____

CAMPGROUND ☆☆☆☆☆

Campground Name: _____

Address: _____

Phone: _____ GPS: _____

Site #: _____ Ideal Site # (for next time): _____

Cost: _____ ☐ day ☐ week ☐ month

Memberships: _____

Altitude: _____ ☐ First Visit ☐ Return Visit

DRIVEWAY LENGTH:

☐ easy access
☐ loop
☐ paved
☐ unpaved-graded
☐ picnic table
☐ fire ring
☐ water
☐ sewer
☐ electricity
☐ 15 amp
☐ 30 amp
☐ 50 amp

☐ back-in
☐ pull-through
☐ restrooms
☐ pet friendly
☐ shade-partial/full
☐ full sun
☐ laundry
☐ store/visitor center
☐ pool/hot tub
☐ hiking trails
☐ fishing
☐ firewood

☐ antenna reception
☐ satellite tv
☐ cable tv
☐ wifi:
  ☐ free ☐ $_____

cell phone carrier:
_____

phone reception
☆☆☆☆☆
water pressure
☆☆☆☆☆

NOTES FOR NEXT TIME

(fees, check in/out times, discounts, directions, loud/quiet, etc)

NOTES

(Campground Pros/Cons, Traveling Companions, People Met, Places Visited,
Things to Do, Restaurants, Journaling):

RV LOG

DATE: ☼ ⛅ ☁ ☂ ⚡ ❄ 🌬 □Hot □Cold □Mild

Traveled from _____ to _____

Route Taken: _____

Start Mileage: _____ End Mileage: _____ Total Miles Traveled: _____

Sites Along The Way:

CAMPGROUND ☆☆☆☆☆

Campground Name: _____

Address: _____

Phone: _____ GPS: _____

Site #: _____ Ideal Site # (for next time): _____

Cost: _____ □ day □ week □ month

Memberships: _____

Altitude: _____ □ First Visit □ Return Visit

DRIVEWAY LENGTH:

□easy access	□back-in	□antenna reception
□loop	□pull-through	□satellite tv
□paved	□restrooms	□cable tv
□unpaved-graded	□pet friendly	□wifi:
□picnic table	□shade-partial/full	□free □$_____
□fire ring	□full sun	cell phone carrier:
□water	□laundry	
□sewer	□store/visitor center	
□electricity	□pool/hot tub	phone reception
□15 amp	□hiking trails	☆☆☆☆☆
□30 amp	□fishing	water pressure
□50 amp	□firewood	☆☆☆☆☆

NOTES FOR NEXT TIME

(fees, check in/out times, discounts, directions, loud/quiet, etc)

NOTES

(Campground Pros/Cons, Traveling Companions, People Met, Places Visited,
Things to Do, Restaurants, Journaling):

RV LOG

DATE: ☀ ⛅ ☁ 🌧 ⛈ ❄ 🌫 ☐Hot ☐Cold ☐Mild

Traveled from _____ to _____

Route Taken: _____

Start Mileage: _____ End Mileage: _____ Total Miles Traveled: _____

Sites Along The Way:

CAMPGROUND ☆☆☆☆☆

Campground Name: _____

Address: _____

Phone: _____ GPS: _____

Site #: _____ Ideal Site # (for next time): _____

Cost: _____ ☐ day ☐ week ☐ month

Memberships: _____

Altitude: _____ ☐ First Visit ☐ Return Visit

DRIVEWAY LENGTH:

☐easy access ☐back-in ☐antenna reception
☐loop ☐pull-through ☐satellite tv
☐paved ☐restrooms ☐cable tv
☐unpaved-graded ☐pet friendly ☐wifi:
☐picnic table ☐shade-partial/full   ☐free ☐$____
☐fire ring ☐full sun cell phone carrier:
☐water ☐laundry
☐sewer ☐store/visitor center _____
☐electricity ☐pool/hot tub phone reception
☐15 amp ☐hiking trails ☆☆☆☆☆
☐30 amp ☐fishing water pressure
☐50 amp ☐firewood ☆☆☆☆☆

NOTES FOR NEXT TIME

(fees, check in/out times, discounts, directions, loud/quiet, etc)

NOTES

(Campground Pros/Cons, Traveling Companions, People Met, Places Visited, Things to Do, Restaurants, Journaling):

RV LOG

DATE: ☀ ⛅ ☁ 🌧 ⛈ ❄ 🌬 □Hot □Cold □Mild

Traveled from _____ to _____

Route Taken: _____

Start Mileage: _____ End Mileage: _____ Total Miles Traveled: _____

Sites Along The Way:

CAMPGROUND ☆☆☆☆☆

Campground Name: _____

Address: _____

Phone: _____ GPS: _____

Site #: _____ Ideal Site # (for next time): _____

Cost: _____ □ day □ week □ month

Memberships: _____

Altitude: _____ □ First Visit □ Return Visit

DRIVEWAY LENGTH:

□ easy access □ back-in □ antenna reception
□ loop □ pull-through □ satellite tv
□ paved □ restrooms □ cable tv
□ unpaved-graded □ pet friendly □ wifi:
□ picnic table □ shade-partial/full □ free □ $____
□ fire ring □ full sun **cell phone carrier:**
□ water □ laundry
□ sewer □ store/visitor center _____
□ electricity □ pool/hot tub **phone reception**
□ 15 amp □ hiking trails ☆☆☆☆☆
□ 30 amp □ fishing **water pressure**
□ 50 amp □ firewood ☆☆☆☆☆

NOTES FOR NEXT TIME

(fees, check in/out times, discounts, directions, loud/quiet, etc)

NOTES

(Campground Pros/Cons, Traveling Companions, People Met, Places Visited,
Things to Do, Restaurants, Journaling):

RV LOG

DATE: ☀ ⛅ ☁ 🌧 ⛈ ❄ 🌫 ☐Hot ☐Cold ☐Mild

Traveled from _____ to _____

Route Taken: _____

Start Mileage: _____ End Mileage: _____ Total Miles Traveled: _____

Sites Along The Way:

CAMPGROUND ☆☆☆☆☆

Campground Name:

Address:

Phone: _____ GPS:

Site #: _____ Ideal Site # (for next time): _____

Cost: _____ ☐ day ☐ week ☐ month

Memberships:

Altitude: _____ ☐ First Visit ☐ Return Visit

DRIVEWAY LENGTH:

☐easy access   ☐back-in   ☐antenna reception
☐loop   ☐pull-through   ☐satellite tv
☐paved   ☐restrooms   ☐cable tv
☐unpaved-graded   ☐pet friendly   ☐wifi:
☐picnic table   ☐shade-partial/full   ☐free ☐$____
☐fire ring   ☐full sun   cell phone carrier:
☐water   ☐laundry
☐sewer   ☐store/visitor center _____
☐electricity   ☐pool/hot tub   phone reception
☐15 amp   ☐hiking trails   ☆☆☆☆☆
☐30 amp   ☐fishing   water pressure
☐50 amp   ☐firewood   ☆☆☆☆☆

NOTES FOR NEXT TIME

(fees, check in/out times, discounts, directions, loud/quiet, etc)

NOTES

(Campground Pros/Cons, Traveling Companions, People Met, Places Visited, Things to Do, Restaurants, Journaling):

RV LOG

DATE: ☀ ⛅ ☁ 🌧 ⛈ ❄ 🌫 ☐Hot ☐Cold ☐Mild

Traveled from _____ to _____

Route Taken: _____

Start Mileage: _____ End Mileage: _____ Total Miles Traveled: _____

Sites Along The Way: _____

CAMPGROUND ☆☆☆☆☆

Campground Name: _____

Address: _____

Phone: _____ GPS: _____

Site #: _____ Ideal Site # (for next time): _____

Cost: _____ ☐ day   ☐ week   ☐ month

Memberships: _____

Altitude: _____   ☐ First Visit   ☐ Return Visit

DRIVEWAY LENGTH: _____

☐easy access	☐back-in	☐antenna reception
☐loop	☐pull-through	☐satellite tv
☐paved	☐restrooms	☐cable tv
☐unpaved-graded	☐pet friendly	☐wifi:
☐picnic table	☐shade-partial/full	☐free ☐$____
☐fire ring	☐full sun	cell phone carrier:
☐water	☐laundry	
☐sewer	☐store/visitor center	_____
☐electricity	☐pool/hot tub	phone reception
☐15 amp	☐hiking trails	☆☆☆☆☆
☐30 amp	☐fishing	water pressure
☐50 amp	☐firewood	☆☆☆☆☆

NOTES FOR NEXT TIME

(fees, check in/out times, discounts, directions, loud/quiet, etc)

NOTES

(Campground Pros/Cons, Traveling Companions, People Met, Places Visited,
Things to Do, Restaurants, Journaling):

RV LOG

DATE: ☼ ⛅ ☁ 🌧 ⛈ ❄ 🌬 ☐Hot ☐Cold ☐Mild

Traveled from _____ to _____

Route Taken: _____

Start Mileage: _____ End Mileage: _____ Total Miles Traveled: _____

Sites Along The Way: _____

CAMPGROUND ☆☆☆☆☆

Campground Name: _____

Address: _____

Phone: _____ GPS: _____

Site #: _____ Ideal Site # (for next time): _____

Cost: _____ ☐ day ☐ week ☐ month

Memberships: _____

Altitude: _____ ☐ First Visit ☐ Return Visit

DRIVEWAY LENGTH:

☐ easy access ☐ back-in ☐ antenna reception
☐ loop ☐ pull-through ☐ satellite tv
☐ paved ☐ restrooms ☐ cable tv
☐ unpaved-graded ☐ pet friendly ☐ wifi:
☐ picnic table ☐ shade-partial/full   ☐ free ☐$_____
☐ fire ring ☐ full sun **cell phone carrier:**
☐ water ☐ laundry
☐ sewer ☐ store/visitor center _____
☐ electricity ☐ pool/hot tub **phone reception**
☐ 15 amp ☐ hiking trails ☆☆☆☆☆
☐ 30 amp ☐ fishing **water pressure**
☐ 50 amp ☐ firewood ☆☆☆☆☆

NOTES FOR NEXT TIME

(fees, check in/out times, discounts, directions, loud/quiet, etc)

NOTES

(Campground Pros/Cons, Traveling Companions, People Met, Places Visited,
Things to Do, Restaurants, Journaling):

RV LOG

DATE: ☀ ⛅ ☁ 🌧 ⛈ ❄ 🌫 ☐Hot ☐Cold ☐Mild

Traveled from _____ to _____

Route Taken: _____

Start Mileage: _____ End Mileage: _____ Total Miles Traveled: _____

Sites Along The Way: _____

CAMPGROUND ☆☆☆☆☆

Campground Name: _____

Address: _____

Phone: _____ GPS: _____

Site #: _____ Ideal Site # (for next time): _____

Cost: _____ ☐ day ☐ week ☐ month

Memberships: _____

Altitude: _____ ☐ First Visit ☐ Return Visit

DRIVEWAY LENGTH:

☐ easy access ☐ back-in ☐ antenna reception
☐ loop ☐ pull-through ☐ satellite tv
☐ paved ☐ restrooms ☐ cable tv
☐ unpaved-graded ☐ pet friendly ☐ wifi:
☐ picnic table ☐ shade-partial/full ☐ free ☐ $_____
☐ fire ring ☐ full sun cell phone carrier:
☐ water ☐ laundry
☐ sewer ☐ store/visitor center _____
☐ electricity ☐ pool/hot tub phone reception
☐ 15 amp ☐ hiking trails ☆☆☆☆☆
☐ 30 amp ☐ fishing water pressure
☐ 50 amp ☐ firewood ☆☆☆☆☆

NOTES FOR NEXT TIME

(fees, check in/out times, discounts, directions, loud/quiet, etc)

NOTES

(Campground Pros/Cons, Traveling Companions, People Met, Places Visited,
Things to Do, Restaurants, Journaling):

RV LOG

DATE: ☼ ⛅ ☁ 🌧 ⛈ ❄ 🌫 ☐Hot ☐Cold ☐Mild

Traveled from _____ to _____

Route Taken: _____

Start Mileage: _____ End Mileage: _____ Total Miles Traveled: _____

Sites Along The Way: _____

CAMPGROUND ☆☆☆☆☆

Campground Name: _____

Address: _____

Phone: _____ GPS: _____

Site #: _____ Ideal Site # (for next time): _____

Cost: _____ ☐ day ☐ week ☐ month

Memberships: _____

Altitude: _____ ☐ First Visit ☐ Return Visit

DRIVEWAY LENGTH:

☐ easy access   ☐ back-in   ☐ antenna reception
☐ loop   ☐ pull-through   ☐ satellite tv
☐ paved   ☐ restrooms   ☐ cable tv
☐ unpaved-graded   ☐ pet friendly   ☐ wifi:
☐ picnic table   ☐ shade-partial/full   ☐ free ☐ $____
☐ fire ring   ☐ full sun   cell phone carrier:
☐ water   ☐ laundry
☐ sewer   ☐ store/visitor center _____
☐ electricity   ☐ pool/hot tub   phone reception
☐ 15 amp   ☐ hiking trails   ☆☆☆☆☆
☐ 30 amp   ☐ fishing   water pressure
☐ 50 amp   ☐ firewood   ☆☆☆☆☆

NOTES FOR NEXT TIME

(fees, check in/out times, discounts, directions, loud/quiet, etc)

NOTES

(Campground Pros/Cons, Traveling Companions, People Met, Places Visited, Things to Do, Restaurants, Journaling):

RV LOG

DATE: ☀ ⛅ ☁ 🌧 ⛈ ❄ 🌫 ☐Hot ☐Cold ☐Mild

Traveled from _____ to _____

Route Taken: _____

Start Mileage: _____ End Mileage: _____ Total Miles Traveled: _____

Sites Along The Way: _____

CAMPGROUND ☆☆☆☆☆

Campground Name: _____

Address: _____

Phone: _____ GPS: _____

Site #: _____ Ideal Site # (for next time): _____

Cost: _____ ☐ day ☐ week ☐ month

Memberships: _____

Altitude: _____ ☐ First Visit ☐ Return Visit

DRIVEWAY LENGTH:

☐ easy access   ☐ back-in   ☐ antenna reception
☐ loop   ☐ pull-through   ☐ satellite tv
☐ paved   ☐ restrooms   ☐ cable tv
☐ unpaved-graded   ☐ pet friendly   ☐ wifi:
☐ picnic table   ☐ shade-partial/full   ☐ free   ☐ $____
☐ fire ring   ☐ full sun
☐ water   ☐ laundry   **cell phone carrier:**
☐ sewer   ☐ store/visitor center   _____
☐ electricity   ☐ pool/hot tub   **phone reception**
☐ 15 amp   ☐ hiking trails   ☆☆☆☆☆
☐ 30 amp   ☐ fishing   **water pressure**
☐ 50 amp   ☐ firewood   ☆☆☆☆☆

NOTES FOR NEXT TIME

(fees, check in/out times, discounts, directions, loud/quiet, etc)

NOTES

(Campground Pros/Cons, Traveling Companions, People Met, Places Visited, Things to Do, Restaurants, Journaling):

RV LOG

DATE: ☀ ⛅ ☁ 🌧 ⛈ ❄ 🌫 ☐Hot ☐Cold ☐Mild

Traveled from _____ to _____

Route Taken: _____

Start Mileage: _____ End Mileage: _____ Total Miles Traveled: _____

Sites Along The Way: _____

CAMPGROUND ☆☆☆☆☆

Campground Name: _____

Address: _____

Phone: _____ GPS: _____

Site #: _____ Ideal Site # (for next time): _____

Cost: _____ ☐ day ☐ week ☐ month

Memberships: _____

Altitude: _____ ☐ First Visit ☐ Return Visit

DRIVEWAY LENGTH:

☐easy access ☐back-in ☐antenna reception
☐loop ☐pull-through ☐satellite tv
☐paved ☐restrooms ☐cable tv
☐unpaved-graded ☐pet friendly ☐wifi:
☐picnic table ☐shade-partial/full ☐free ☐$_____
☐fire ring ☐full sun **cell phone carrier:**
☐water ☐laundry
☐sewer ☐store/visitor center _____
☐electricity ☐pool/hot tub **phone reception**
☐15 amp ☐hiking trails ☆☆☆☆☆
☐30 amp ☐fishing **water pressure**
☐50 amp ☐firewood ☆☆☆☆☆

NOTES FOR NEXT TIME

(fees, check in/out times, discounts, directions, loud/quiet, etc)

NOTES

(Campground Pros/Cons, Traveling Companions, People Met, Places Visited, Things to Do, Restaurants, Journaling):

RV LOG

DATE: ☀ ⛅ ☁ 🌧 ⛈ ❄ 🌫 ☐Hot ☐Cold ☐Mild

Traveled from _____ to _____

Route Taken: _____

Start Mileage: _____ End Mileage: _____ Total Miles Traveled: _____

Sites Along The Way: _____

CAMPGROUND ☆☆☆☆☆

Campground Name: _____

Address: _____

Phone: _____ GPS: _____

Site #: _____ Ideal Site # (for next time): _____

Cost: _____ ☐ day ☐ week ☐ month

Memberships: _____

Altitude: _____ ☐ First Visit ☐ Return Visit

DRIVEWAY LENGTH:

☐ easy access   ☐ back-in   ☐ antenna reception
☐ loop   ☐ pull-through   ☐ satellite tv
☐ paved   ☐ restrooms   ☐ cable tv
☐ unpaved-graded   ☐ pet friendly   ☐ wifi:
☐ picnic table   ☐ shade-partial/full   ☐ free ☐ $____
☐ fire ring   ☐ full sun   cell phone carrier:
☐ water   ☐ laundry
☐ sewer   ☐ store/visitor center   _____
☐ electricity   ☐ pool/hot tub   phone reception
☐ 15 amp   ☐ hiking trails   ☆☆☆☆☆
☐ 30 amp   ☐ fishing   water pressure
☐ 50 amp   ☐ firewood   ☆☆☆☆☆

NOTES FOR NEXT TIME

(fees, check in/out times, discounts, directions, loud/quiet, etc)

NOTES

(Campground Pros/Cons, Traveling Companions, People Met, Places Visited,
Things to Do, Restaurants, Journaling):

RV LOG

DATE: ☀ ⛅ ☁ 🌧 ⛈ ❄ 🌬 ☐Hot ☐Cold ☐Mild

Traveled from _____ to _____

Route Taken: _____

Start Mileage: _____ End Mileage: _____ Total Miles Traveled: _____

Sites Along The Way: _____

CAMPGROUND ☆☆☆☆☆

Campground Name: _____

Address: _____

Phone: _____ GPS: _____

Site #: _____ Ideal Site # (for next time): _____

Cost: _____ ☐ day ☐ week ☐ month

Memberships: _____

Altitude: _____ ☐ First Visit ☐ Return Visit

DRIVEWAY LENGTH:

☐ easy access
☐ loop
☐ paved
☐ unpaved-graded
☐ picnic table
☐ fire ring
☐ water
☐ sewer
☐ electricity
☐ 15 amp
☐ 30 amp
☐ 50 amp

☐ back-in
☐ pull-through
☐ restrooms
☐ pet friendly
☐ shade-partial/full
☐ full sun
☐ laundry
☐ store/visitor center
☐ pool/hot tub
☐ hiking trails
☐ fishing
☐ firewood

☐ antenna reception
☐ satellite tv
☐ cable tv
☐ wifi:
  ☐ free ☐ $____

cell phone carrier:
_____

phone reception
☆☆☆☆☆
water pressure
☆☆☆☆☆

NOTES FOR NEXT TIME

(fees, check in/out times, discounts, directions, loud/quiet, etc)

NOTES

(Campground Pros/Cons, Traveling Companions, People Met, Places Visited,
Things to Do, Restaurants, Journaling):

RV LOG

DATE: ☼ ☁ ☁ ☂ ☇ ❄ ☁ ☐Hot ☐Cold ☐Mild

Traveled from _____ to _____

Route Taken: _____

Start Mileage: _____ End Mileage: _____ Total Miles Traveled: _____

Sites Along The Way: _____

CAMPGROUND ☆☆☆☆☆

Campground Name: _____

Address: _____

Phone: _____ GPS: _____

Site #: _____ Ideal Site # (for next time): _____

Cost: _____ ☐ day ☐ week ☐ month

Memberships: _____

Altitude: _____ ☐ First Visit ☐ Return Visit

DRIVEWAY LENGTH:

☐ easy access ☐ back-in ☐ antenna reception
☐ loop ☐ pull-through ☐ satellite tv
☐ paved ☐ restrooms ☐ cable tv
☐ unpaved-graded ☐ pet friendly ☐ wifi:
☐ picnic table ☐ shade-partial/full ☐ free ☐$____
☐ fire ring ☐ full sun
☐ water ☐ laundry cell phone carrier:
☐ sewer ☐ store/visitor center _____
☐ electricity ☐ pool/hot tub phone reception
☐ 15 amp ☐ hiking trails ☆☆☆☆☆
☐ 30 amp ☐ fishing water pressure
☐ 50 amp ☐ firewood ☆☆☆☆☆

NOTES FOR NEXT TIME

(fees, check in/out times, discounts, directions, loud/quiet, etc)

NOTES

(Campground Pros/Cons, Traveling Companions, People Met, Places Visited,
Things to Do, Restaurants, Journaling):

RV LOG

DATE: ☀ ⛅ ☁ 🌦 🌧 ❄ 🌬 ☐Hot ☐Cold ☐Mild

Traveled from _____ to _____

Route Taken: _____

Start Mileage: _____ End Mileage: _____ Total Miles Traveled: _____

Sites Along The Way:

CAMPGROUND ☆☆☆☆☆

Campground Name: _____

Address: _____

Phone: _____ GPS: _____

Site #: _____ Ideal Site # (for next time): _____

Cost: _____ ☐ day ☐ week ☐ month

Memberships: _____

Altitude: _____ ☐ First Visit ☐ Return Visit

DRIVEWAY LENGTH:

☐easy access	☐back-in	☐antenna reception
☐loop	☐pull-through	☐satellite tv
☐paved	☐restrooms	☐cable tv
☐unpaved-graded	☐pet friendly	☐wifi:
☐picnic table	☐shade-partial/full	☐free ☐$_____
☐fire ring	☐full sun	cell phone carrier:
☐water	☐laundry	
☐sewer	☐store/visitor center	_____
☐electricity	☐pool/hot tub	phone reception
☐15 amp	☐hiking trails	☆☆☆☆☆
☐30 amp	☐fishing	water pressure
☐50 amp	☐firewood	☆☆☆☆☆

NOTES FOR NEXT TIME

(fees, check in/out times, discounts, directions, loud/quiet, etc)

NOTES

(Campground Pros/Cons, Traveling Companions, People Met, Places Visited,
Things to Do, Restaurants, Journaling):

RV LOG

DATE: ☀️ 🌤️ ☁️ 🌦️ 🌧️ ❄️ 🌬️ ☐Hot ☐Cold ☐Mild

Traveled from _____ to _____

Route Taken: _____

Start Mileage: _____ End Mileage: _____ Total Miles Traveled: _____

Sites Along The Way: _____

CAMPGROUND ☆☆☆☆☆

Campground Name: _____

Address: _____

Phone: _____ GPS: _____

Site #: _____ Ideal Site # (for next time): _____

Cost: _____ ☐ day ☐ week ☐ month

Memberships: _____

Altitude: _____ ☐ First Visit ☐ Return Visit

DRIVEWAY LENGTH:

☐ easy access ☐ back-in   ☐ antenna reception
☐ loop   ☐ pull-through   ☐ satellite tv
☐ paved   ☐ restrooms   ☐ cable tv
☐ unpaved-graded ☐ pet friendly   ☐ wifi:
☐ picnic table ☐ shade-partial/full   ☐ free ☐ $____
☐ fire ring   ☐ full sun   cell phone carrier:
☐ water   ☐ laundry
☐ sewer   ☐ store/visitor center _____
☐ electricity   ☐ pool/hot tub   phone reception
☐ 15 amp   ☐ hiking trails   ☆☆☆☆☆
☐ 30 amp   ☐ fishing   water pressure
☐ 50 amp   ☐ firewood   ☆☆☆☆☆

NOTES FOR NEXT TIME

(fees, check in/out times, discounts, directions, loud/quiet, etc)

NOTES

(Campground Pros/Cons, Traveling Companions, People Met, Places Visited, Things to Do, Restaurants, Journaling):

RV LOG

DATE: ☀ ☁ ☁ ☂ ☔ ❄ ☁ ☐Hot ☐Cold ☐Mild

Traveled from _____ to _____

Route Taken: _____

Start Mileage: _____ End Mileage: _____ Total Miles Traveled: _____

Sites Along The Way:

CAMPGROUND ☆☆☆☆☆

Campground Name: _____

Address: _____

Phone: _____ GPS: _____

Site #: _____ Ideal Site # (for next time): _____

Cost: _____ ☐ day ☐ week ☐ month

Memberships: _____

Altitude: _____ ☐ First Visit ☐ Return Visit

DRIVEWAY LENGTH:

☐easy access ☐back-in ☐antenna reception
☐loop ☐pull-through ☐satellite tv
☐paved ☐restrooms ☐cable tv
☐unpaved-graded ☐pet friendly ☐wifi:
☐picnic table ☐shade-partial/full   ☐free ☐$____
☐fire ring ☐full sun   cell phone carrier:
☐water ☐laundry
☐sewer ☐store/visitor center _____
☐electricity ☐pool/hot tub   phone reception
☐15 amp ☐hiking trails   ☆☆☆☆☆
☐30 amp ☐fishing   water pressure
☐50 amp ☐firewood   ☆☆☆☆☆

NOTES FOR NEXT TIME

(fees, check in/out times, discounts, directions, loud/quiet, etc)

NOTES

(Campground Pros/Cons, Traveling Companions, People Met, Places Visited,
Things to Do, Restaurants, Journaling):

RV LOG

DATE: ☀ ⛅ ☁ 🌧 ⛈ ❄ 🌬 ☐Hot ☐Cold ☐Mild

Traveled from _____ to _____

Route Taken: _____

Start Mileage: _____ End Mileage: _____ Total Miles Traveled: _____

Sites Along The Way:

CAMPGROUND ☆☆☆☆☆

Campground Name: _____

Address: _____

Phone: _____ GPS: _____

Site #: _____ Ideal Site # (for next time): _____

Cost: _____ ☐ day ☐ week ☐ month

Memberships: _____

Altitude: _____ ☐ First Visit ☐ Return Visit

DRIVEWAY LENGTH:

☐ easy access   ☐ back-in   ☐ antenna reception
☐ loop   ☐ pull-through   ☐ satellite tv
☐ paved   ☐ restrooms   ☐ cable tv
☐ unpaved-graded   ☐ pet friendly   ☐ wifi:
☐ picnic table   ☐ shade-partial/full   ☐ free ☐ $_____
☐ fire ring   ☐ full sun   cell phone carrier:
☐ water   ☐ laundry
☐ sewer   ☐ store/visitor center   _____
☐ electricity   ☐ pool/hot tub   phone reception
☐ 15 amp   ☐ hiking trails   ☆☆☆☆☆
☐ 30 amp   ☐ fishing   water pressure
☐ 50 amp   ☐ firewood   ☆☆☆☆☆

NOTES FOR NEXT TIME

(fees, check in/out times, discounts, directions, loud/quiet, etc)

NOTES

(Campground Pros/Cons, Traveling Companions, People Met, Places Visited,
Things to Do, Restaurants, Journaling):

RV LOG

DATE: ☼ ⛅ ☁ 🌧 ⚡ ❄ 🌫 ☐Hot ☐Cold ☐Mild

Traveled from .... to ....

Route Taken: ....

Start Mileage: .... End Mileage: .... Total Miles Traveled: ....

Sites Along The Way: ....

CAMPGROUND ☆☆☆☆☆

Campground Name: ....

Address: ....

Phone: .... GPS: ....

Site #: .... Ideal Site # (for next time): ....

Cost: .... ☐ day   ☐ week   ☐ month

Memberships: ....

Altitude: .... ☐ First Visit   ☐ Return Visit

DRIVEWAY LENGTH:

☐easy access	☐back-in	☐antenna reception
☐loop	☐pull-through	☐satellite tv
☐paved	☐restrooms	☐cable tv
☐unpaved-graded	☐pet friendly	☐wifi:
☐picnic table	☐shade-partial/full	☐free ☐$____
☐fire ring	☐full sun	cell phone carrier:
☐water	☐laundry	
☐sewer	☐store/visitor center	_____
☐electricity	☐pool/hot tub	phone reception
☐15 amp	☐hiking trails	☆☆☆☆☆
☐30 amp	☐fishing	water pressure
☐50 amp	☐firewood	☆☆☆☆☆

NOTES FOR NEXT TIME

(fees, check in/out times, discounts, directions, loud/quiet, etc)

NOTES

(Campground Pros/Cons, Traveling Companions, People Met, Places Visited, Things to Do, Restaurants, Journaling):

RV LOG

DATE: ☀ ⛅ ☁ 🌧 ⛈ ❄ 🌫 ☐Hot ☐Cold ☐Mild

Traveled from _____ to _____

Route Taken: _____

Start Mileage: _____ End Mileage: _____ Total Miles Traveled: _____

Sites Along The Way:

CAMPGROUND ☆☆☆☆☆

Campground Name: _____

Address: _____

Phone: _____ GPS: _____

Site #: _____ Ideal Site # (for next time): _____

Cost: _____ ☐ day   ☐ week   ☐ month

Memberships: _____

Altitude: _____ ☐ First Visit   ☐ Return Visit

DRIVEWAY LENGTH:

☐easy access	☐back-in	☐antenna reception
☐loop	☐pull-through	☐satellite tv
☐paved	☐restrooms	☐cable tv
☐unpaved-graded	☐pet friendly	☐wifi:
☐picnic table	☐shade-partial/full	☐free ☐$____
☐fire ring	☐full sun	cell phone carrier:
☐water	☐laundry	
☐sewer	☐store/visitor center	_____
☐electricity	☐pool/hot tub	phone reception
☐15 amp	☐hiking trails	☆☆☆☆☆
☐30 amp	☐fishing	water pressure
☐50 amp	☐firewood	☆☆☆☆☆

NOTES FOR NEXT TIME

(fees, check in/out times, discounts, directions, loud/quiet, etc)

NOTES

(Campground Pros/Cons, Traveling Companions, People Met, Places Visited,
Things to Do, Restaurants, Journaling):

RV LOG

DATE: ☀ ⛅ ☁ 🌧 ⛈ ❄ 🌬 ☐Hot ☐Cold ☐Mild

Traveled from _____ to _____

Route Taken: _____

Start Mileage: _____ End Mileage: _____ Total Miles Traveled: _____

Sites Along The Way: _____

CAMPGROUND ☆☆☆☆☆

Campground Name: _____

Address: _____

Phone: _____ GPS: _____

Site #: _____ Ideal Site # (for next time): _____

Cost: _____ ☐ day ☐ week ☐ month

Memberships: _____

Altitude: _____ ☐ First Visit ☐ Return Visit

DRIVEWAY LENGTH:

☐easy access	☐back-in	☐antenna reception
☐loop	☐pull-through	☐satellite tv
☐paved	☐restrooms	☐cable tv
☐unpaved-graded	☐pet friendly	☐wifi:
☐picnic table	☐shade-partial/full	☐free ☐$____
☐fire ring	☐full sun	cell phone carrier:
☐water	☐laundry	
☐sewer	☐store/visitor center	_____
☐electricity	☐pool/hot tub	phone reception
☐15 amp	☐hiking trails	☆☆☆☆☆
☐30 amp	☐fishing	water pressure
☐50 amp	☐firewood	☆☆☆☆☆

NOTES FOR NEXT TIME

(fees, check in/out times, discounts, directions, loud/quiet, etc)

NOTES

(Campground Pros/Cons, Traveling Companions, People Met, Places Visited, Things to Do, Restaurants, Journaling):

RV LOG

DATE: ☀️ ⛅ ☁️ 🌧️ ⚡ ❄️ 🌬️ ☐Hot ☐Cold ☐Mild

Traveled from _____ to _____

Route Taken: _____

Start Mileage: _____ End Mileage: _____ Total Miles Traveled: _____

Sites Along The Way: _____

CAMPGROUND ☆☆☆☆☆

Campground Name: _____

Address: _____

Phone: _____ GPS: _____

Site #: _____ Ideal Site # (for next time): _____

Cost: _____ ☐ day ☐ week ☐ month

Memberships: _____

Altitude: _____ ☐ First Visit ☐ Return Visit

DRIVEWAY LENGTH:

☐ easy access
☐ loop
☐ paved
☐ unpaved-graded
☐ picnic table
☐ fire ring
☐ water
☐ sewer
☐ electricity
☐ 15 amp
☐ 30 amp
☐ 50 amp

☐ back-in
☐ pull-through
☐ restrooms
☐ pet friendly
☐ shade-partial/full
☐ full sun
☐ laundry
☐ store/visitor center
☐ pool/hot tub
☐ hiking trails
☐ fishing
☐ firewood

☐ antenna reception
☐ satellite tv
☐ cable tv
☐ wifi:
    ☐ free ☐ $_____

cell phone carrier:

_____

phone reception
☆☆☆☆☆
water pressure
☆☆☆☆☆

NOTES FOR NEXT TIME

(fees, check in/out times, discounts, directions, loud/quiet, etc)

NOTES

(Campground Pros/Cons, Traveling Companions, People Met, Places Visited,
Things to Do, Restaurants, Journaling):

RV LOG

DATE: ☼ ⛅ ☁ 🌧 ⛈ ❄ 🌬 ☐Hot ☐Cold ☐Mild

Traveled from _____ to _____

Route Taken: _____

Start Mileage: _____ End Mileage: _____ Total Miles Traveled: _____

Sites Along The Way:

CAMPGROUND ☆☆☆☆☆

Campground Name: _____

Address: _____

Phone: _____ GPS: _____

Site #: _____ Ideal Site # (for next time): _____

Cost: _____ ☐ day   ☐ week   ☐ month

Memberships: _____

Altitude: _____ ☐ First Visit   ☐ Return Visit

DRIVEWAY LENGTH:

☐ easy access
☐ loop
☐ paved
☐ unpaved-graded
☐ picnic table
☐ fire ring
☐ water
☐ sewer
☐ electricity
☐ 15 amp
☐ 30 amp
☐ 50 amp

☐ back-in
☐ pull-through
☐ restrooms
☐ pet friendly
☐ shade-partial/full
☐ full sun
☐ laundry
☐ store/visitor center
☐ pool/hot tub
☐ hiking trails
☐ fishing
☐ firewood

☐ antenna reception
☐ satellite tv
☐ cable tv
☐ wifi:
☐ free ☐ $_____

cell phone carrier:

_____

phone reception
☆☆☆☆☆
water pressure
☆☆☆☆☆

NOTES FOR NEXT TIME

(fees, check in/out times, discounts, directions, loud/quiet, etc)

NOTES

(Campground Pros/Cons, Traveling Companions, People Met, Places Visited,
Things to Do, Restaurants, Journaling):

RV LOG

DATE: ☼ ⛅ ☁ ☂ ⚡ ❄ 🌀 ☐Hot ☐Cold ☐Mild

Traveled from _____ to _____

Route Taken: _____

Start Mileage: _____ End Mileage: _____ Total Miles Traveled: _____

Sites Along The Way:

CAMPGROUND ☆☆☆☆☆

Campground Name: _____

Address: _____

Phone: _____ GPS: _____

Site #: _____ Ideal Site # (for next time): _____

Cost: _____ ☐ day ☐ week ☐ month

Memberships: _____

Altitude: _____ ☐ First Visit ☐ Return Visit

DRIVEWAY LENGTH:

☐easy access	☐back-in	☐antenna reception
☐loop	☐pull-through	☐satellite tv
☐paved	☐restrooms	☐cable tv
☐unpaved-graded	☐pet friendly	☐wifi:
☐picnic table	☐shade-partial/full	☐free ☐$_____
☐fire ring	☐full sun	cell phone carrier:
☐water	☐laundry	
☐sewer	☐store/visitor center	_____
☐electricity	☐pool/hot tub	phone reception
☐15 amp	☐hiking trails	☆☆☆☆☆
☐30 amp	☐fishing	water pressure
☐50 amp	☐firewood	☆☆☆☆☆

NOTES FOR NEXT TIME

(fees, check in/out times, discounts, directions, loud/quiet, etc)

NOTES

(Campground Pros/Cons, Traveling Companions, People Met, Places Visited,
Things to Do, Restaurants, Journaling):

RV LOG

DATE: ☀ ⛅ ☁ 🌧 ⛈ ❄ 🌫 ☐Hot ☐Cold ☐Mild

Traveled from _____ to _____

Route Taken: _____

Start Mileage: _____ End Mileage: _____ Total Miles Traveled: _____

Sites Along The Way:

CAMPGROUND ☆☆☆☆☆

Campground Name: _____

Address: _____

Phone: _____ GPS: _____

Site #: _____ Ideal Site # (for next time): _____

Cost: _____ ☐ day ☐ week ☐ month

Memberships: _____

Altitude: _____ ☐ First Visit ☐ Return Visit

DRIVEWAY LENGTH:

☐ easy access
☐ loop
☐ paved
☐ unpaved-graded
☐ picnic table
☐ fire ring
☐ water
☐ sewer
☐ electricity
☐ 15 amp
☐ 30 amp
☐ 50 amp

☐ back-in
☐ pull-through
☐ restrooms
☐ pet friendly
☐ shade-partial/full
☐ full sun
☐ laundry
☐ store/visitor center
☐ pool/hot tub
☐ hiking trails
☐ fishing
☐ firewood

☐ antenna reception
☐ satellite tv
☐ cable tv
☐ wifi:
  ☐ free ☐ $_____

cell phone carrier:
_____

phone reception
☆☆☆☆☆
water pressure
☆☆☆☆☆

NOTES FOR NEXT TIME

(fees, check in/out times, discounts, directions, loud/quiet, etc)

NOTES

(Campground Pros/Cons, Traveling Companions, People Met, Places Visited,
Things to Do, Restaurants, Journaling):

RV LOG

DATE: ☀ ⛅ ☁ 🌧 ⛈ ❄ 🌫 ☐Hot ☐Cold ☐Mild

Traveled from _____ to _____

Route Taken: _____

Start Mileage: _____ End Mileage: _____ Total Miles Traveled: _____

Sites Along The Way:

CAMPGROUND ☆☆☆☆☆

Campground Name: _____

Address: _____

Phone: _____ GPS: _____

Site #: _____ Ideal Site # (for next time): _____

Cost: _____ ☐ day ☐ week ☐ month

Memberships: _____

Altitude: _____ ☐ First Visit ☐ Return Visit

DRIVEWAY LENGTH:

☐ easy access
☐ loop
☐ paved
☐ unpaved-graded
☐ picnic table
☐ fire ring
☐ water
☐ sewer
☐ electricity
☐ 15 amp
☐ 30 amp
☐ 50 amp

☐ back-in
☐ pull-through
☐ restrooms
☐ pet friendly
☐ shade-partial/full
☐ full sun
☐ laundry
☐ store/visitor center
☐ pool/hot tub
☐ hiking trails
☐ fishing
☐ firewood

☐ antenna reception
☐ satellite tv
☐ cable tv
☐ wifi:
  ☐ free ☐ $_____
cell phone carrier:

_____
phone reception
☆☆☆☆☆
water pressure
☆☆☆☆☆

NOTES FOR NEXT TIME

(fees, check in/out times, discounts, directions, loud/quiet, etc)

NOTES

(Campground Pros/Cons, Traveling Companions, People Met, Places Visited,
Things to Do, Restaurants, Journaling):

RV LOG

DATE: ☼ ⛅ ☁ 🌧 ⛈ ❄ 🌬 ☐Hot ☐Cold ☐Mild

Traveled from _____ to _____

Route Taken: _____

Start Mileage: _____ End Mileage: _____ Total Miles Traveled: _____

Sites Along The Way:

CAMPGROUND ☆☆☆☆☆

Campground Name: _____

Address: _____

Phone: _____ GPS: _____

Site #: _____ Ideal Site # (for next time): _____

Cost: _____ ☐ day ☐ week ☐ month

Memberships: _____

Altitude: _____ ☐ First Visit ☐ Return Visit

DRIVEWAY LENGTH:

☐ easy access   ☐ back-in   ☐ antenna reception
☐ loop   ☐ pull-through   ☐ satellite tv
☐ paved   ☐ restrooms   ☐ cable tv
☐ unpaved-graded   ☐ pet friendly   ☐ wifi:
☐ picnic table   ☐ shade-partial/full   ☐ free   ☐ $____
☐ fire ring   ☐ full sun   cell phone carrier:
☐ water   ☐ laundry
☐ sewer   ☐ store/visitor center   _____
☐ electricity   ☐ pool/hot tub   phone reception
☐ 15 amp   ☐ hiking trails   ☆☆☆☆☆
☐ 30 amp   ☐ fishing   water pressure
☐ 50 amp   ☐ firewood   ☆☆☆☆☆

NOTES FOR NEXT TIME

(fees, check in/out times, discounts, directions, loud/quiet, etc)

NOTES

(Campground Pros/Cons, Traveling Companions, People Met, Places Visited,
Things to Do, Restaurants, Journaling):

RV LOG

DATE: ☀ ⛅ ☁ ☂ ⛈ ❄ 🌫 ☐Hot ☐Cold ☐Mild

Traveled from _____ to _____

Route Taken: _____

Start Mileage: _____ End Mileage: _____ Total Miles Traveled: _____

Sites Along The Way:

CAMPGROUND ☆☆☆☆☆

Campground Name: _____

Address: _____

Phone: _____ GPS: _____

Site #: _____ Ideal Site # (for next time): _____

Cost: _____ ☐ day ☐ week ☐ month

Memberships: _____

Altitude: _____ ☐ First Visit ☐ Return Visit

DRIVEWAY LENGTH:

☐easy access ☐back-in ☐antenna reception
☐loop ☐pull-through ☐satellite tv
☐paved ☐restrooms ☐cable tv
☐unpaved-graded ☐pet friendly ☐wifi:
☐picnic table ☐shade-partial/full ☐free ☐$____
☐fire ring ☐full sun cell phone carrier:
☐water ☐laundry
☐sewer ☐store/visitor center _____
☐electricity ☐pool/hot tub phone reception
☐15 amp ☐hiking trails ☆☆☆☆☆
☐30 amp ☐fishing water pressure
☐50 amp ☐firewood ☆☆☆☆☆

NOTES FOR NEXT TIME

(fees, check in/out times, discounts, directions, loud/quiet, etc)

NOTES

(Campground Pros/Cons, Traveling Companions, People Met, Places Visited,
Things to Do, Restaurants, Journaling):

RV LOG

DATE: ☀ ⛅ ☁ 🌧 ⛈ ❄ 🌬 ☐Hot ☐Cold ☐Mild

Traveled from _____ to _____

Route Taken: _____

Start Mileage: _____ End Mileage: _____ Total Miles Traveled: _____

Sites Along The Way:

CAMPGROUND ☆☆☆☆☆

Campground Name: _____

Address: _____

Phone: _____ GPS: _____

Site #: _____ Ideal Site # (for next time): _____

Cost: _____ ☐ day ☐ week ☐ month

Memberships: _____

Altitude: _____ ☐ First Visit ☐ Return Visit

DRIVEWAY LENGTH:

☐easy access ☐back-in ☐antenna reception
☐loop ☐pull-through ☐satellite tv
☐paved ☐restrooms ☐cable tv
☐unpaved-graded ☐pet friendly ☐wifi:
☐picnic table ☐shade-partial/full   ☐free ☐$_____
☐fire ring ☐full sun cell phone carrier:
☐water ☐laundry
☐sewer ☐store/visitor center _____
☐electricity ☐pool/hot tub phone reception
☐15 amp ☐hiking trails ☆☆☆☆☆
☐30 amp ☐fishing water pressure
☐50 amp ☐firewood ☆☆☆☆☆

NOTES FOR NEXT TIME

(fees, check in/out times, discounts, directions, loud/quiet, etc)

NOTES

(Campground Pros/Cons, Traveling Companions, People Met, Places Visited,
Things to Do, Restaurants, Journaling):

RV LOG

DATE: ☀️ ⛅ ☁️ 🌧️ ⛈️ ❄️ 🌬️ ☐Hot ☐Cold ☐Mild

Traveled from _____ to _____

Route Taken: _____

Start Mileage: _____ End Mileage: _____ Total Miles Traveled: _____

Sites Along The Way: _____

CAMPGROUND ☆☆☆☆☆

Campground Name: _____

Address: _____

Phone: _____ GPS: _____

Site #: _____ Ideal Site # (for next time): _____

Cost: _____ ☐ day ☐ week ☐ month

Memberships: _____

Altitude: _____ ☐ First Visit ☐ Return Visit

DRIVEWAY LENGTH:

☐easy access   ☐back-in   ☐antenna reception
☐loop   ☐pull-through   ☐satellite tv
☐paved   ☐restrooms   ☐cable tv
☐unpaved-graded ☐pet friendly   ☐wifi:
☐picnic table   ☐shade-partial/full   ☐free ☐$_____
☐fire ring   ☐full sun   cell phone carrier:
☐water   ☐laundry
☐sewer   ☐store/visitor center _____
☐electricity   ☐pool/hot tub   phone reception
☐15 amp   ☐hiking trails   ☆☆☆☆☆
☐30 amp   ☐fishing   water pressure
☐50 amp   ☐firewood   ☆☆☆☆☆

NOTES FOR NEXT TIME
(fees, check in/out times, discounts, directions, loud/quiet, etc)

NOTES

(Campground Pros/Cons, Traveling Companions, People Met, Places Visited, Things to Do, Restaurants, Journaling):

RV LOG

DATE: ☀ ⛅ ☁ 🌧 ⛈ ❄ 🌫 ☐Hot ☐Cold ☐Mild

Traveled from _____ to _____

Route Taken: _____

Start Mileage: _____ End Mileage: _____ Total Miles Traveled: _____

Sites Along The Way:

CAMPGROUND ☆☆☆☆☆

Campground Name: _____

Address: _____

Phone: _____ GPS: _____

Site #: _____ Ideal Site # (for next time): _____

Cost: _____ ☐ day ☐ week ☐ month

Memberships: _____

Altitude: _____ ☐ First Visit ☐ Return Visit

DRIVEWAY LENGTH:

☐ easy access
☐ loop
☐ paved
☐ unpaved-graded
☐ picnic table
☐ fire ring
☐ water
☐ sewer
☐ electricity
☐ 15 amp
☐ 30 amp
☐ 50 amp

☐ back-in
☐ pull-through
☐ restrooms
☐ pet friendly
☐ shade-partial/full
☐ full sun
☐ laundry
☐ store/visitor center
☐ pool/hot tub
☐ hiking trails
☐ fishing
☐ firewood

☐ antenna reception
☐ satellite tv
☐ cable tv
☐ wifi:
  ☐ free ☐ $_____

cell phone carrier:

_____

phone reception
☆☆☆☆☆
water pressure
☆☆☆☆☆

NOTES FOR NEXT TIME

(fees, check in/out times, discounts, directions, loud/quiet, etc)

NOTES

(Campground Pros/Cons, Traveling Companions, People Met, Places Visited,
Things to Do, Restaurants, Journaling):

RV LOG

DATE: ☀ ⛅ ☁ 🌧 ⛈ ❄ 🌫 ☐Hot ☐Cold ☐Mild

Traveled from _____ to _____

Route Taken: _____

Start Mileage: _____ End Mileage: _____ Total Miles Traveled: _____

Sites Along The Way:

CAMPGROUND ☆☆☆☆☆

Campground Name: _____

Address: _____

Phone: _____ GPS: _____

Site #: _____ Ideal Site # (for next time): _____

Cost: _____ ☐ day ☐ week ☐ month

Memberships: _____

Altitude: _____ ☐ First Visit ☐ Return Visit

DRIVEWAY LENGTH:

☐easy access	☐back-in	☐antenna reception
☐loop	☐pull-through	☐satellite tv
☐paved	☐restrooms	☐cable tv
☐unpaved-graded	☐pet friendly	☐wifi:
☐picnic table	☐shade-partial/full	☐free ☐$____
☐fire ring	☐full sun	cell phone carrier:
☐water	☐laundry	
☐sewer	☐store/visitor center	_____
☐electricity	☐pool/hot tub	phone reception
☐15 amp	☐hiking trails	☆☆☆☆☆
☐30 amp	☐fishing	water pressure
☐50 amp	☐firewood	☆☆☆☆☆

NOTES FOR NEXT TIME

(fees, check in/out times, discounts, directions, loud/quiet, etc)

NOTES

(Campground Pros/Cons, Traveling Companions, People Met, Places Visited, Things to Do, Restaurants, Journaling):

RV LOG

DATE: ☀ ⛅ ☁ 🌧 ⚡ ❄ 🌫 ☐Hot ☐Cold ☐Mild

Traveled from _____ to _____

Route Taken: _____

Start Mileage: _____ End Mileage: _____ Total Miles Traveled: _____

Sites Along The Way:

CAMPGROUND ☆☆☆☆☆

Campground Name: _____

Address: _____

Phone: _____ GPS: _____

Site #: _____ Ideal Site # (for next time): _____

Cost: _____ ☐ day ☐ week ☐ month

Memberships: _____

Altitude: _____ ☐ First Visit ☐ Return Visit

DRIVEWAY LENGTH:

☐easy access ☐back-in ☐antenna reception
☐loop ☐pull-through ☐satellite tv
☐paved ☐restrooms ☐cable tv
☐unpaved-graded ☐pet friendly ☐wifi:
☐picnic table ☐shade-partial/full ☐free ☐$_____
☐fire ring ☐full sun cell phone carrier:
☐water ☐laundry
☐sewer ☐store/visitor center _____
☐electricity ☐pool/hot tub phone reception
☐15 amp ☐hiking trails ☆☆☆☆☆
☐30 amp ☐fishing water pressure
☐50 amp ☐firewood ☆☆☆☆☆

NOTES FOR NEXT TIME

(fees, check in/out times, discounts, directions, loud/quiet, etc)

NOTES

(Campground Pros/Cons, Traveling Companions, People Met, Places Visited,
Things to Do, Restaurants, Journaling):

RV LOG

DATE: ☀ ⛅ ☁ 🌧 ⛈ ❄ 🌬 ☐Hot ☐Cold ☐Mild

Traveled from _____ to _____

Route Taken: _____

Start Mileage: _____ End Mileage: _____ Total Miles Traveled: _____

Sites Along The Way: _____

CAMPGROUND ☆☆☆☆☆

Campground Name: _____

Address: _____

Phone: _____ GPS: _____

Site #: _____ Ideal Site # (for next time): _____

Cost: _____ ☐ day ☐ week ☐ month

Memberships: _____

Altitude: _____ ☐ First Visit ☐ Return Visit

DRIVEWAY LENGTH:

☐easy access ☐back-in ☐antenna reception
☐loop ☐pull-through ☐satellite tv
☐paved ☐restrooms ☐cable tv
☐unpaved-graded ☐pet friendly ☐wifi:
☐picnic table ☐shade-partial/full ☐free ☐$____
☐fire ring ☐full sun
☐water ☐laundry cell phone carrier:
☐sewer ☐store/visitor center _____
☐electricity ☐pool/hot tub phone reception
☐15 amp ☐hiking trails ☆☆☆☆☆
☐30 amp ☐fishing water pressure
☐50 amp ☐firewood ☆☆☆☆☆

NOTES FOR NEXT TIME

(fees, check in/out times, discounts, directions, loud/quiet, etc)

NOTES

(Campground Pros/Cons, Traveling Companions, People Met, Places Visited,
Things to Do, Restaurants, Journaling):

RV   LOG

DATE: ☀ ⛅ ☁ 🌧 ⛈ ❄ 🌬 ☐Hot ☐Cold ☐Mild

Traveled from _____ to _____

Route Taken: _____

Start Mileage: _____ End Mileage: _____ Total Miles Traveled: _____

Sites Along The Way: _____

CAMPGROUND ☆☆☆☆☆

Campground Name: _____

Address: _____

Phone: _____ GPS: _____

Site #: _____ Ideal Site # (for next time): _____

Cost: _____ ☐ day ☐ week ☐ month

Memberships: _____

Altitude: _____ ☐ First Visit ☐ Return Visit

DRIVEWAY LENGTH:

☐ easy access   ☐ back-in   ☐ antenna reception
☐ loop   ☐ pull-through   ☐ satellite tv
☐ paved   ☐ restrooms   ☐ cable tv
☐ unpaved-graded   ☐ pet friendly   ☐ wifi:
☐ picnic table   ☐ shade-partial/full   ☐ free ☐ $_____
☐ fire ring   ☐ full sun
☐ water   ☐ laundry   cell phone carrier:
☐ sewer   ☐ store/visitor center
☐ electricity   ☐ pool/hot tub   _____
☐ 15 amp   ☐ hiking trails   phone reception
☐ 30 amp   ☐ fishing   ☆☆☆☆☆
☐ 50 amp   ☐ firewood   water pressure ☆☆☆☆☆

NOTES FOR NEXT TIME

(fees, check in/out times, discounts, directions, loud/quiet, etc)

NOTES

(Campground Pros/Cons, Traveling Companions, People Met, Places Visited,
Things to Do, Restaurants, Journaling):

RV LOG

DATE: ☀ ⛅ ☁ 🌧 ⛈ ❄ 🌬 ☐Hot ☐Cold ☐Mild

Traveled from _____ to _____

Route Taken: _____

Start Mileage: _____ End Mileage: _____ Total Miles Traveled: _____

Sites Along The Way:

CAMPGROUND ☆☆☆☆☆

Campground Name: _____

Address: _____

Phone: _____ GPS: _____

Site #: _____ Ideal Site # (for next time): _____

Cost: _____ ☐ day ☐ week ☐ month

Memberships: _____

Altitude: _____ ☐ First Visit ☐ Return Visit

DRIVEWAY LENGTH:

☐ easy access ☐ back-in ☐ antenna reception
☐ loop ☐ pull-through ☐ satellite tv
☐ paved ☐ restrooms ☐ cable tv
☐ unpaved-graded ☐ pet friendly ☐ wifi:
☐ picnic table ☐ shade-partial/full   ☐ free ☐ $____
☐ fire ring ☐ full sun   cell phone carrier:
☐ water ☐ laundry
☐ sewer ☐ store/visitor center _____
☐ electricity ☐ pool/hot tub   phone reception
☐ 15 amp ☐ hiking trails   ☆☆☆☆☆
☐ 30 amp ☐ fishing   water pressure
☐ 50 amp ☐ firewood   ☆☆☆☆☆

NOTES FOR NEXT TIME

(fees, check in/out times, discounts, directions, loud/quiet, etc)

NOTES

(Campground Pros/Cons, Traveling Companions, People Met, Places Visited,
Things to Do, Restaurants, Journaling):

RV LOG

DATE: ☀ ⛅ ☁ 🌦 🌧 ❄ 🌫 ☐Hot ☐Cold ☐Mild

Traveled from _____ to _____

Route Taken: _____

Start Mileage: _____ End Mileage: _____ Total Miles Traveled: _____

Sites Along The Way: _____

CAMPGROUND   ☆ ☆ ☆ ☆ ☆

Campground Name: _____

Address: _____

Phone: _____ GPS: _____

Site #: _____ Ideal Site # (for next time): _____

Cost: _____ ☐ day   ☐ week   ☐ month

Memberships: _____

Altitude: _____ ☐ First Visit   ☐ Return Visit

DRIVEWAY LENGTH:

☐easy access	☐back-in	☐antenna reception
☐loop	☐pull-through	☐satellite tv
☐paved	☐restrooms	☐cable tv
☐unpaved-graded	☐pet friendly	☐wifi:
☐picnic table	☐shade-partial/full	☐free ☐$____
☐fire ring	☐full sun	cell phone carrier:
☐water	☐laundry	
☐sewer	☐store/visitor center	_____
☐electricity	☐pool/hot tub	phone reception
☐15 amp	☐hiking trails	☆ ☆ ☆ ☆ ☆
☐30 amp	☐fishing	water pressure
☐50 amp	☐firewood	☆ ☆ ☆ ☆ ☆

NOTES FOR NEXT TIME

(fees, check in/out times, discounts, directions, loud/quiet, etc)

NOTES

(Campground Pros/Cons, Traveling Companions, People Met, Places Visited, Things to Do, Restaurants, Journaling):

RV LOG

DATE: ☀ ⛅ ☁ ☂ ⚡ ❄ 🌬 ☐Hot ☐Cold ☐Mild

Traveled from _____ to _____

Route Taken: _____

Start Mileage: _____ End Mileage: _____ Total Miles Traveled: _____

Sites Along The Way:

CAMPGROUND ☆☆☆☆☆

Campground Name: _____

Address: _____

Phone: _____ GPS: _____

Site #: _____ Ideal Site # (for next time): _____

Cost: _____ ☐ day ☐ week ☐ month

Memberships: _____

Altitude: _____ ☐ First Visit ☐ Return Visit

DRIVEWAY LENGTH:

☐ easy access
☐ loop
☐ paved
☐ unpaved-graded
☐ picnic table
☐ fire ring
☐ water
☐ sewer
☐ electricity
☐ 15 amp
☐ 30 amp
☐ 50 amp

☐ back-in
☐ pull-through
☐ restrooms
☐ pet friendly
☐ shade-partial/full
☐ full sun
☐ laundry
☐ store/visitor center
☐ pool/hot tub
☐ hiking trails
☐ fishing
☐ firewood

☐ antenna reception
☐ satellite tv
☐ cable tv
☐ wifi:
　☐ free ☐ $____

cell phone carrier:

_____

phone reception
☆☆☆☆☆
water pressure
☆☆☆☆☆

NOTES FOR NEXT TIME

(fees, check in/out times, discounts, directions, loud/quiet, etc)

NOTES

(Campground Pros/Cons, Traveling Companions, People Met, Places Visited,
Things to Do, Restaurants, Journaling):

Made in the USA
Coppell, TX
26 November 2022